"Did you have a bad day, Bird?" said Skunk.
"I did," said Bird. "I need to rest,
but I can't get up to my nest."

"We'll get you up there," said Skunk.
"I will make a plan.
Then if we all do a little,
we can be a big help."

“See the little tree?” said Skunk.
“Who can get it down for me?”

"I'll get the little tree down," said Beaver.
"If we all do a little, we can be a big help."

"See the big tree?" said Skunk.
"Who can get the little tree
over to the big tree?"

“I’ll get it over there,” said Deer.
“If we all do a little, we can be a big help.”

"See the nest in the big tree?" said Beaver.
"Who can get the little tree up to the nest?"
"I'll get it up there," said Snake.

"You all did a little, and you were a big help!" said Bird.